KU-424-840

ROBERT LOUIS STEVENSON'S

TREASURE ISLAND

by Robert Louis Stevenson
retold by Wim Coleman and Pat Perrin
illustrated by Greg Rebis

Librarian Reviewer
Allyson A.W. Lyga MS
Library Media/Graphic Novel Consultant

Reading Consultant
Mark DeYoung
Classroom Teacher

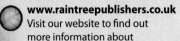

www.raintreepublishers.co.uk
Visit our website to find out
more information about
Raintree books.

To order:
☎ Phone +44 (0) 1865 888066
▤ Fax +44 (0) 1865 314091
▣ Visit www.raintreepublishers.co.uk

Raintree is an imprint of Capstone Global Library Limited, a company incorporated in England and Wales having its registered office at 7 Pilgrim Street, London, EC4V 6LB – Registered company number: 6695582

Art Director: Heather Kindseth
Graphic Designers: Heather Kindseth and Kay Fraser
Colourists: Greg Rebis, Dylan Edwards, Tiffany Moore,
Leila Hill, Melissa Armstrong and Catherine Rebis
Edited in the UK by Laura Knowles
Printed and bound in China by Leo Paper Products Ltd

ISBN 978-1406212501 (hardback)
13 12 11 10 09
10 9 8 7 6 5 4 3 2 1

British Library Cataloguing in Publication Data
Coleman, Wim.
Treasure Island. -- 2nd ed. -- (Graphic revolve)
741.5-dc22
A full catalogue record for this book is available from the British Library.

TABLE OF CONTENTS

INTRODUCING . . .

Jim Hawkins

Ben Gunn

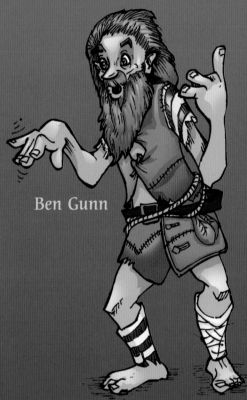

Billy Bones

Dr Livesey

4

Mr Trelawney

Captain Smollett

Long John Silver

Israel Hands

11

The men sneak away from the *Hispaniola* . . .

. . . but the few pirates aboard the ship soon discover their plan.

They're firing on us!

Were you shipwrecked on this island?

Not exactly. I was left behind by my mates while looking for Cap'n Flint's treasure.

Is that Cap'n Flint's ship offshore?

No, Flint's dead, but some of his men are aboard it.

Ben Gunn quickly shares his story. He had been part of Captain Flint's crew, along with Long John Silver and Billy Bones, when Flint buried his treasure on the island.

Not a man with one leg? If he finds me, I'm dead for sure.

Three years ago, I came back to this island, looking for the treasure, and it took me that long to find it.

If your captain promises to take me home, I'll share my treasure.

We'll all be rich, rich, **rich!**

The next morning . . .

Ben Gunn says he can help us, but he seems a little crazy.

Well lad, he has been stranded here for three years! But it sounds like we can trust him.

As Jim and Dr Livesey talk . . .

Flag of truce!

It's Silver himself!

I bet it's a trick.

By the time the fighting ends, only eight pirates are left alive. Five of the crew remain, but the captain is badly hurt.

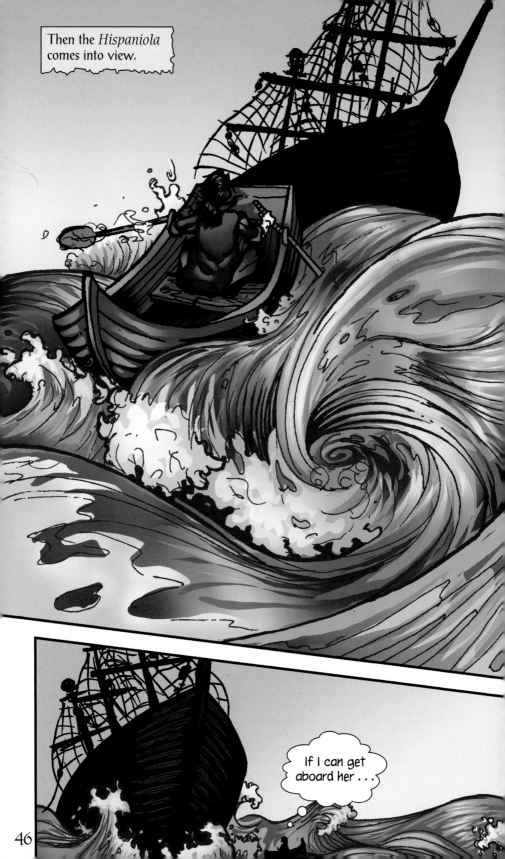

Just then the ship crashes into the shore.

CREEEEEEEAK KRUNCH

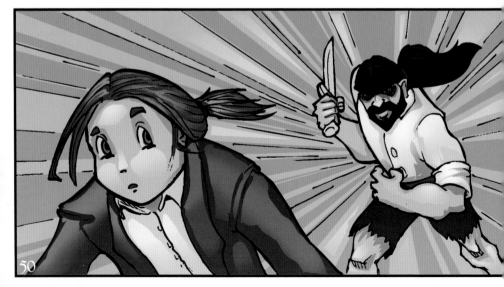

51

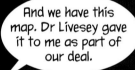

Inside Ben Gunn's cave . . .

It'll take us a few days to get all this aboard the *Hispaniola*.

After they load the treasure onto the ship, Captain Smollett, Dr Livesey, Mr Trelawney, Long John Silver, and Jim Hawkins sail away from Treasure Island.

Don't leave us!

We needn't waste our pity on those dogs!

For once I agree with you, Silver.

The *Hispaniola* sails to a port in Mexico, where Captain Smollett hires some new crew members.

While the ship is in port, Long John escapes.

I did it! I helped him escape. If Silver had stayed aboard, we'd have ended up dead.

Jim Hawkins and his mother live comfortably on their share.

Jim never sees Long John Silver again and lives a happy life. But sometimes, in his worst dreams, he hears a high-pitched voice ringing in his ears . . .

Pieces of eight! Squawk! Pieces of eight!

About Robert Louis Stevenson

Robert Louis Stevenson was born in 1850 in Edinburgh, Scotland. He enjoyed travelling and having adventures. During one family holiday, Stevenson and his stepson amused themselves by drawing a treasure map for an imaginary island. The stories he and his stepson told inspired Stevenson to write *Treasure Island*. It was published in 1883. Stevenson's other famous books include *Kidnapped* and *The Strange Case of Dr Jekyll and Mr Hyde*. He died in 1894.

About the Retelling Authors

Wim Coleman and Pat Perrin are a married couple who love writing books together. They have written many young adult non-fiction and fiction books, including retellings of classic novels, stories, and myths. They run a scholarship program for Mexican students and live in Guanajuato, Mexico.

About the Illustrator

Greg Rebis was born in New York, USA, but grew up mostly in central Florida. After working in civic government, pizza delivery, music retail and proofreading, he eventually began to work in publishing, film and graphics. He currently lives and studies in Rhode Island, USA and still loves art, sci-fi and video games.

Glossary

ashore (ah-SHOR) – on or towards the shore or land

beach (BEECH) – to land a ship on the shore

curiosity (kyur-ee-OHSS-i-tee) – wanting to know more about things

Hispaniola (HISS-span-ee-oh-la) – Captain Smollett's ship

inn (IN) – a small hotel, often with a restaurant

magistrate (MAJ-ih-strate) – a government official or judge who has the power to enforce the law

mate (MAYT) – a friend or person that someone works with

pieces of eight (PEESS-iz uhv ATE) – in pirate times, the Spanish currency was the peso, which was worth eight reales. Sometimes, a pirate would break the peso coin into eight pieces to make change.

request (re-KWEST) – something that is asked for

seaman (SEE-man) – a sailor

shipwrecked (SHIP-rekd) – a ship that has been destroyed at sea

tending to (TEN-ding TOO) – taking care of

truce (TROOS) – an agreement to stop fighting

BACKGROUND OF TREASURE ISLAND

In the 1700s, the world of Jim Hawkins was full of sailing ships. People crossed the oceans, transported goods, and explored new lands using wind power and strong ocean currents. In seaside towns, ships were loaded along the wharves, or docks. A captain called his ship "shipshape" or "seaworthy" if it was ready to go to sea. And when the captain yelled "all hands on deck," the crew boarded, ready to work.

Each person on a ship had their own special job to do. Cabin boys, hoping to learn more about sailing, served the captain. The captain steered the ship by turning the ship's tiller. Crew members would lift and lower the heavy sails. To keep the ship in one place, the crew would drop an anchor, or heavy weight. If a ship went adrift, meaning that it floated off course, the crew sometimes stopped it by sailing it onto land, or beaching it. The life of a sailor was hard, and not all crew members made it home alive.

Ships travelled on the "high seas," waters that were not owned by any country. Life at sea was full of danger. A ship could sink in a storm or become shipwrecked. Crews could be stranded on strange islands or coastlines. Pirates could attack. To show they were in command of a ship, pirates would "raise the Jolly Roger," hang a black flag with a skull and crossbones from a high mast.

Discussion Questions

1. Why did Billy Bones die?

2. How did Jim figure out that Long John Silver was the one-legged pirate that Billy Bones told him about?

3. What would you do if you found buried treasure?

4. Why did Jim sneak onto one of the small boats when the pirates went to look for buried treasure?

WRITING PROMPTS

1. At the end of the story, the pirates flee and the remaining crew members of the *Hispaniola* divide the treasure. How did each person spend the treasure? What does this tell you about each person?

2. Describe your favourite character in *Treasure Island*. Why do you like this character? Would you want to sail on a ship with this person?

3. If you could pick any place in the world to have an adventure, where would you go? Explain how you would get there and what you would discover.

Other Books

Robin Hood

Robin Hood and his Merrie Men are the heroes of Sherwood Forest. Taking from the rich and giving to the poor, Robin Hood and his loyal followers fight for the downtrodden and oppressed. As they outwit the cruel Sheriff of Nottingham, Robin Hood and his Merrie Men are led on a series of exciting adventures.

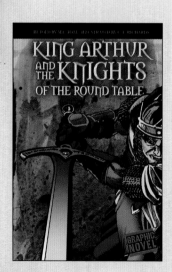

King Arthur and the Knights of the Round Table

In a world of wizards, giants, and dragons, King Arthur and the Knights of the Round Table are the kingdom of Camelot's only defence against the threatening forces of evil. Fighting battles and saving those in need, the Knights of the Round Table can defeat every enemy but one – themselves!

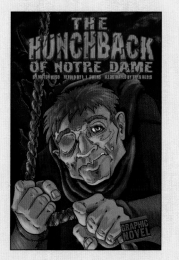

The Hunchback of Notre Dame

Hidden away in the bell tower of the Cathedral of Notre Dame, Quasimodo is treated like a beast. Although he is gentle and kind, he has the reputation of a frightening monster because of his physical deformities. He develops affection for Esmeralda, a gypsy girl who shows him kindness in return. When the girl is sentenced to an unfair death by hanging, Quasimodo is determined to save her. But those closest to Quasimodo have other plans for the gypsy.

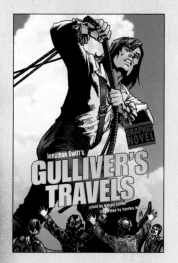

Gulliver's Travels

Lemuel Gulliver always dreamed of sailing across seas, but he never could have imagined the places his travels would take him. On the island of Lilliput, he is captured by tiny creatures no more than six inches tall. In a country of Blefuscu, he is nearly squashed by an army of giants. His adventures could be the greatest tales ever told, if he survives long enough to tell them.

GRAPHIC REVOLVE

If you have enjoyed this story, there are many more exciting tales for you to discover in the Graphic Revolve collection...

20,000 Leagues Under the Sea

Black Beauty

Dracula

Frankenstein

Gulliver's Travels

The Hound of the Baskervilles

The Hunchback of Notre Dame

King Arthur and the Knights of the Round Table

Robin Hood

The Strange Case of Dr Jekyll and Mr Hyde

Treasure Island

The War of the Worlds